GEOMETRIC
Constructions
and Investigations
with a
Mira®

Ernest Woodward and Thomas Hamel

 **J. Weston Walch, Publisher**
Portland, Maine

Users' Guide
to
Walch Reproducible Books

As part of our general effort to provide educational materials which are as practical and economical as possible, we have designated this publication a "reproducible book." The designation means that purchase of the book includes purchase of the right to limited reproduction of all pages on which this symbol appears:

Here is the basic Walch policy: We grant to individual purchasers of this book the right to make sufficient copies of reproducible pages for use by all students of a single teacher. This permission is limited to a single teacher, and does not apply to entire schools or school systems, so institutions purchasing the book should pass the permission on to a single teacher. Copying of the book or its parts for resale is prohibited.

Any questions regarding this policy or requests to purchase further reproduction rights should be addressed to:

Permissions Editor
J. Weston Walch, Publisher
P.O. Box 658
Portland, ME 04104-0658

—*J. Weston Walch, Publisher*

1   2   3   4   5   6   7   8   9   10

ISBN 0-8251-2173-6
Copyright © 1992
J. Weston Walch, Publisher
P.O. Box 658 • Portland, Maine 04104-0658

Printed in the United States of America

Contents

Introduction . . . . *v*

Introduction

In the opinion of the authors, one of the most significant documents written in the last twenty years is the National Council of Teachers of Mathematics (NCTM) publication *Curriculum and Evaluation Standards for School Mathematics.* Here is a quote from page 7 of this publication:

> First "knowing" mathematics is "doing" mathematics. A person gathers, discovers, or creates knowledge in the course of some activity having a purpose. The active process is different from mastering concepts and procedures. We do not assert that informational knowledge has no value, only that its value lies in the extent to which it is useful in the course of some purposeful activity. It is clear that fundamental concepts and procedures from some branches of mathematics should be known by all students; established concepts and procedures can be relied on as fixed variables in a setting in which other variables may be unknown. But instruction should persistently emphasize "doing" rather than "knowing that."

The Mira-oriented lessons contained in this book are certainly consistent with that point of view. These lessons require active participation on the part of students. The authors have used the related activities with students from a wide range of ages and these students have almost universally enjoyed using the Mira. It is a device that has high motivational value.

Geometry is receiving increased emphasis in the professional literature. However, many teachers are still asking the question "What should we teach and how should we teach it?" The following quote from page 112 of the *Standards* provide teachers with very good advice.

> Students discover relationships and develop spatial sense by constructing, drawing, measuring, visualizing, comparing, transforming, and classifying geometric figures. Discussing ideas, conjecturing, and testing hypotheses precede the development of more formal summary statements. In the process, definitions become meaningful, relationships among figures are understood, and students are prepared to use these ideas to develop formal arguments. The informal exploration of geometry can be exciting and mathematically productive for middle school students. At this level, geometry should focus on investigating and using geometric ideas and relationships rather than memorizing definitions and formulas.

While this advice is addressed primarily to middle school mathematics teachers, it is also practical for high school geometry teachers. This is particularly significant in the case of teachers of high school geometry courses in school systems where geometry is not emphasized in middle school. In such cases, some high schools presently have courses entitled "Informal Geometry." The lessons in this booklet provide opportunities for students to construct, draw, visualize, compare, and transform in an informal setting.

What Is a Mira and What Can You Do With It?

The main portion of the Mira is a piece of translucent red acrylic plastic about 9 cm by 15 cm. One of the 15 cm edges is rebated (beveled). The Mira is held upright by two ends also made of plastic. The purpose of the ends is to make the Mira sit perpendicular to the surface being examined. When the Mira is used, the rebated edge must be down and toward the user, and when any line is drawn along an edge of the Mira, it should be drawn along the rebated edge. Since the plastic is translucent, it is possible to see an object on the far side of the Mira in addition to seeing the image of a figure that is on the near side of the Mira.

The most obvious use of the Mira is for line reflections. The rebated edge of the Mira is put on the reflection line and the observed image can be sketched by tracing it on the far side of the Mira while viewing from the near side. Since it is possible to see through the Mira, it is easy to find symmetry lines of plane figures. Also, since the perpendicular bisector of a segment and the bisector of an angle are both symmetry lines, these constructions are trivial. A line perpendicular to a given line through a given point can be readily constructed. Thus, it is possible to use the Mira to construct the bisectors of the angles of a triangle, the altitudes of a triangle, and the perpendicular bisectors of the sides of a triangle. The Mira can be used to construct a line parallel to a given line. Congruent coplanar circles can be identified by making the image of one circle match the other circle. In the case of other coplanar figures such as segments, triangles, and quadri- laterals, congruence can be determined with a Mira only when one figure is the reflection image of the other.

Using the Mira

It is very easy to learn to use the Mira. Generally speaking, the reflection of some figure or part of a figure is required. When this is the case, the Mira is placed between the figure being reflected and the general desired position of the image. The paper is then turned so that the figure is on the side of the Mira closest to the user. Two important points were made above but should be emphasized.

1. **When using the Mira, always place the beveled edge down and toward you.**

2. **When drawing a line along the edge of the Mira, always draw it along the beveled edge.**

Using this Book

This book contains twenty-one geometry lessons in which extensive use of a Mira is required. The general format of each lesson involves some information for the teacher concerning the lesson and some student worksheet pages. The information for the teacher includes a list of prerequisite lessons, a description of needed materials, and some suggestions to the teacher about conducting the lesson. Needed materials usually include only worksheets for each student and a Mira for each student, but occasionally a ruler/straightedge for each student is required, and a few lessons involve the use of a transparency. When a transparency is used, the master of the transparency is included with the materials for the lesson. The edge of the Mira can be used as a straightedge, but it is a little clumsy to use the Mira in this way, so it is recommended that a ruler be used to draw lines.

For each lesson, the transparency and the worksheet pages are numbered to correspond to the number of the lesson. For example, the transparency for Lesson 1 is labeled "Transparency 1," while all the worksheet pages are labeled "Worksheet 1." Worksheet pages after the first one are noted by the word "continued." Since Lesson 2 does not require a transparency, the book does not contain a transparency labeled "Transparency 2."

The "Directions for the Teacher" comments refer to lessons that are to be taught in a large group format with each student having a Mira. Minor adjustments can be made so that the materials can be used with individual students or with small groups of students. In this case, each student or small group of students should be given copies of all transparency pages in addition to all worksheet pages. Depending upon the particular lesson, some verbal directions may be necessary. It is desirable for each student to have a Mira in all learning situations. However, when this is not possible, a pair of students may share a single Mira. If students share a Mira, the teacher should check to see that the Mira is actually shared and both students complete the activity. The "Prerequisite Lessons" suggestions give general directions for sequencing the lessons. The lessons do not necessarily need to be taught in the order in which they appear.

The lessons have varying degrees of difficulty. The first 14 lessons are fairly easy, but lessons 15–21 are quite difficult.

Lesson 1

Introduction to the Mira

Materials Needed

One copy of each of the following pages for each student: pages 3, 4, 5, and 6

One transparency of page 2

One Mira for each student

Directions for the Teacher

Place the transparency on the overhead projector and go through the information given there. Be certain that your students can identify the rebated edge. Emphasize the importance of keeping the rebated edge down and toward them. Also emphasize that when they are to draw a line along an edge of the Mira, it must always be drawn along this rebated edge. This procedure is not particularly important for Lessons 1 and 2, but it is vital for many of the other lessons.

Distribute the first page of Worksheet 1. To complete this activity, the student should place the Mira between the child and the swing, turn the worksheet so the child is on the front side of the Mira, adjust the Mira so the image of the child is on the swing, and then trace the child on the swing. Distribute the other three pages of Worksheet 1. Do not staple these three pages together but give them out individually. Have the students work on one page at a time; when students have finished with one page, direct them to put that page aside. Provide individual assistance as needed.

Transparency 1

The main portion of the Mira has a rebated edge. When using the Mira, place the rebated edge down and toward you so that lines are drawn as shown below.

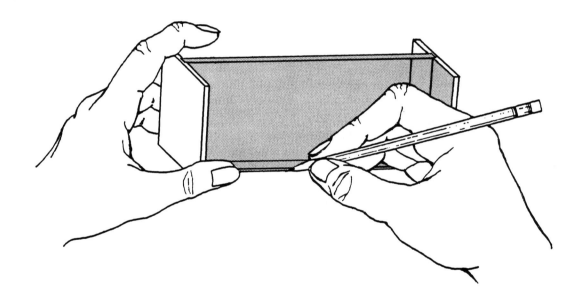

To avoid irregularities, it is recommended that a single sheet be used at a time.

Name _____   Date _____

Worksheet 1

Introduction to the Mira

1. Use the Mira to put the child on the swing. Then reach behind the Mira and trace the child on the swing.

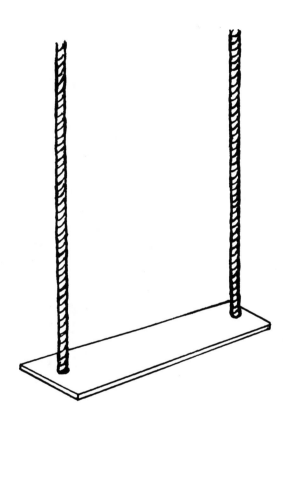

Name _____   Date _____

Introduction to the Mira *(continued)*

2. Using the Mira, put the earring on the woman. Then reach behind the Mira and trace the earring on the woman.

4   *Geometric Constructions and Investigations with a Mira*

Worksheet 1

Introduction to the Mira (continued)

3. Using the Mira, put each hat on the woman. Select the hat you like best and trace it on the woman.

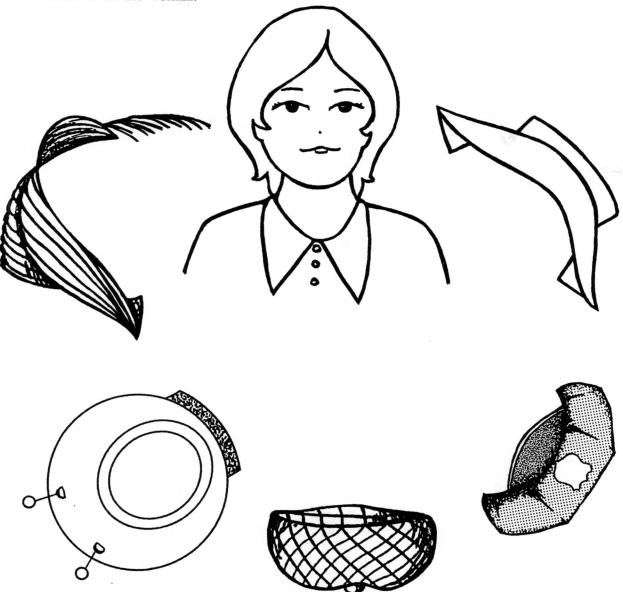

Worksheet 1

Introduction to the Mira *(continued)*

4. Using the Mira, put each hat (helmet, cap) on the man. Select the hat you like best and trace it on the man.

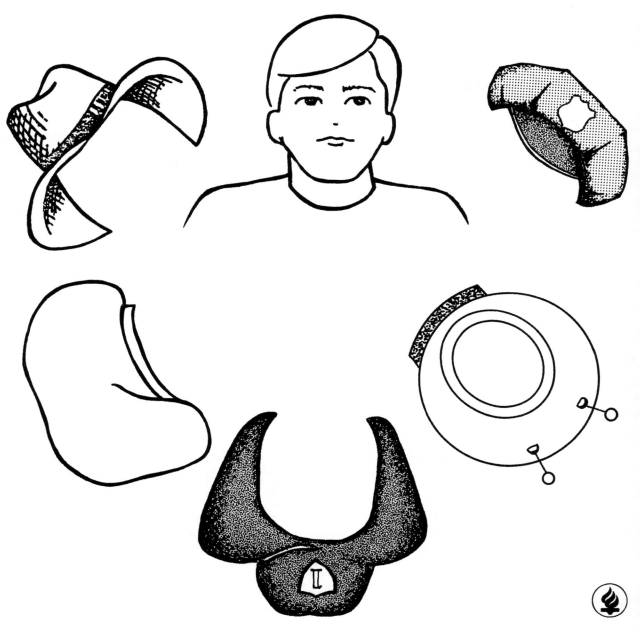

Lesson 2
Reflecting Triangles I

Prerequisite Lessons

Lesson 1

Materials Needed

One copy of page 8 for each student

One Mira for each student

One ruler or straightedge for each student

Directions for the Teacher

Distribute the worksheet and have your students proceed with the problem presented there. One of the purposes of the lesson is to give students experience with the Mira. The fact that one of the image triangles is on the same side of the line as the given triangle, while the other two image triangles are on the other side of the line, may cause some students to experience difficulties. Help them as needed.

Some students may notice the above-mentioned fact and ask questions about the result. At this stage it is recommended that you reward them for being observant, but avoid discussing why. Lesson 17 includes a more complete discussion of this question.

Worksheet 2

Reflecting Triangles I

Place the Mira between the triangle and the line and move it around until the image of side $\overline{BC}$ falls on the line. Reach behind the Mira and mark the points that correspond to A, B, and C. Then use a ruler to draw the new triangle. Repeat the process for sides $\overline{AB}$ and $\overline{AC}$.

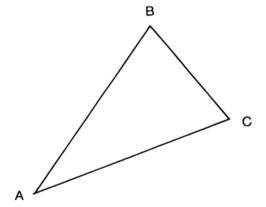

Lesson 3

Line Reflections and Orientation

Prerequisite Lessons

Lessons 1 and 2

Materials Needed

One copy of each of the following pages for each student: pages 11 and 12

One Mira for each student

One ruler or straightedge for each student

Directions for the Teacher

Distribute the worksheet pages and assist the students in using the Mira to find the reflections. Students should put the Mira on the reflection line and draw dots on the far side of the Mira corresponding to vertices of the figures on the near side of the Mira. They should then remove the Mira and use a ruler/straightedge to connect these dots.

After the students have completed the worksheets, direct them back to Problem 1. Tell them to trace △ABC by starting at A, then going to B, then to C, and finally back to A. Ask them which direction they traced the triangle (clockwise). Now tell them to trace △A′B′C′ by starting at A′, then going to B′, then to C′, and finally back to A′. Ask them which direction they traced the triangle (counterclockwise). Have them proceed in a similar way with Problems 2, 3, and 4. In each instance they discover that tracing the original figure and the reflection image involve opposite-direction orientation. Note that in Problem 2, the figure is oriented counterclockwise and the reflection image is oriented clockwise. Next, ask them to return to Problem 1. Tell them to imagine that they are "walking around" △ABC by starting at A, going to B, then going to C, and finally returning to A. Ask them to indicate on which side the region of the triangle is located (right). Then have them imagine walking around △A′B′C′ by starting at A′, going to B′, then going to C′, and finally returning to A′. Ask them to indicate on which side the region of the triangle is located (left). Have them proceed similarly to Problems 2, 3, and 4. They should arrive at comparable conclusions. Note that in Problem 2, the region of △ABC is on the left side as you "walk around" the triangle, while the region of the reflection image is on the right side of the "walk around." Tell them that this illustrates that a figure and the reflection of that figure have opposite orientation.

Name _____ Date _____

Line Reflections and Orientation

1. Find the reflection image of ΔABC about line *l*. Label the new triangle as ΔA'B'C' so that A' corresponds to A, B' corresponds to B, and C' corresponds to C.

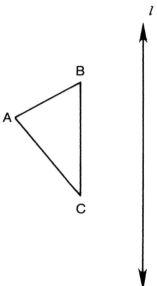

2. Find the reflection image of ΔABC about line *l*. Label the new triangle as ΔA'B'C' so that A' corresponds to A, B' corresponds to B, and C' corresponds to C.

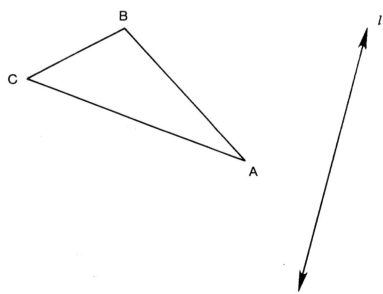

Worksheet 3

Line Reflections and Orientation *(continued)*

3. Find the reflection image of quadrilateral ABCD about line *l*. Label the new quadrilateral A′B′C′D′ so that A′ corresponds to A, B′ corresponds to B, C′ corresponds to C, and D′ corresponds to D.

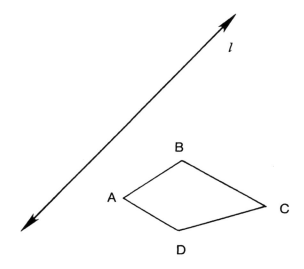

4. Find the reflection image of pentagon ABCDE about line *l*. Label the new pentagon A′B′C′D′E′ so that A′ corresponds to A, B′ corresponds to B, C′ corresponds to C, D′ corresponds to D, and E′ corresponds to E.

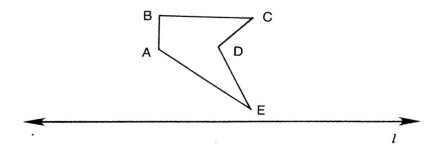

Lesson 4

Symmetry Lines

Prerequisite Lessons

Lesson 1

Materials Needed

One copy of each of the following pages for each student: pages 14, 15, and 16

One pair of scissors for each student

One Mira for each student

Directions for the Teacher

Distribute a copy of the first page of Worksheet 4. Have the students cut out the pentagon pictured there. Tell them that if you cut out a polygon and can fold the cutout so that the two parts match, the fold line is a line of symmetry. Have them fold the pentagon to find lines of symmetry (there are five). Then suggest that the folding method is really not very practical and suggest that they investigate using the Mira. Eventually, they should find that when they put the Mira on a fold line, the image of the front portion of the pentagon matches the rear portion of the pentagon. Distribute the other two worksheet pages and provide individual assistance as needed.

Name _____   Date _____

Worksheet 4

Symmetry Lines

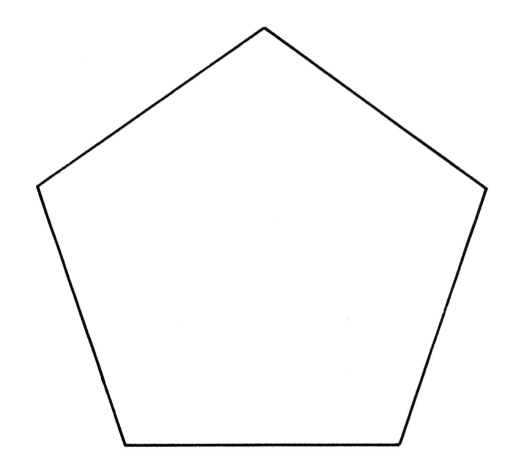

Name _____   Date _____

Worksheet 4

Symmetry Lines *(continued)*

1. Use the Mira to find all lines of symmetry. Draw the symmetry lines along the rebated edge of the Mira.

2. Use the Mira to find several lines of symmetry. Draw these symmetry lines along the rebated edge of the Mira.

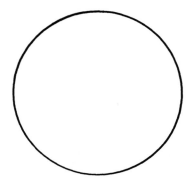

Geometric Constructions and Investigations with a Mira

Worksheet 4

Symmetry Lines *(continued)*

3. Use the Mira to complete the figure so the dotted line is a line of symmetry for the completed figure.

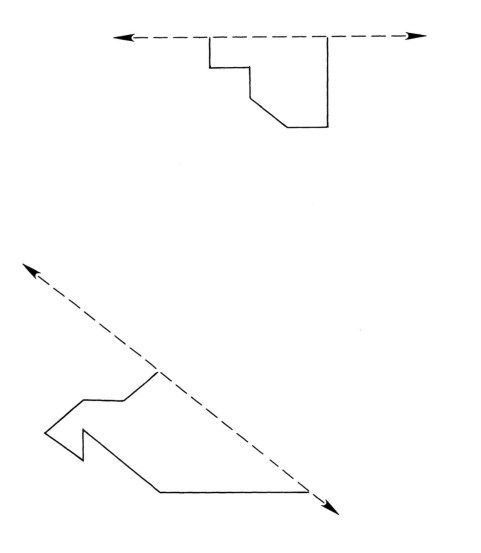

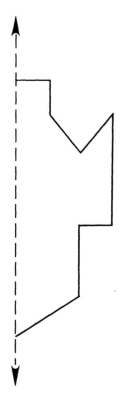

Lesson 5

Symmetry Lines of Triangles

Prerequisite Lessons

Lessons 1 and 4

Materials Needed

One copy of each of the following pages for each student: pages 19, 20, 21, and 22

One ruler or straightedge for each student

One Mira for each student

Directions for the Teacher

Distribute the worksheet pages and tell the students that as they draw triangles, they must have vertices at dots. Direct them to carefully make fairly large triangles using a ruler or straightedge. Correct answers for the activities follow.

(1) A variety of pictures can be drawn, but the triangles must be isosceles triangles.

(2) It is impossible for a triangle to have exactly two lines of symmetry.

(3) A variety of pictures can be drawn, but the triangles must be equilateral triangles.

(4) A variety of pictures can be drawn, but the triangles must be scalene triangles.

After the students have completed the worksheets, lead a discussion concerning the relationship between the number of symmetry lines and the type of triangle. Ask them to consider the possibility of a triangle having more than three lines of symmetry. They should conclude that

(1) a triangle with exactly one symmetry line must be an isosceles triangle,

(2) a triangle cannot have exactly two lines of symmetry,

(3) a triangle with three lines of symmetry must be an equilateral triangle,

(4) a triangle with zero lines of symmetry must be a scalene triangle, and

(5) a triangle cannot have more than three lines of symmetry.

Name _____   Date _____

Worksheet 5

Symmetry Lines of Triangles

1. On the dot paper provided below, draw a picture, if possible, of a large triangle that has exactly one line of symmetry. If you think the triangle you have drawn is correct, check it with a Mira.

```
·    ·    ·    ·    ·    ·    ·    ·

·    ·    ·    ·    ·    ·    ·    ·

·    ·    ·    ·    ·    ·    ·    ·

·    ·    ·    ·    ·    ·    ·    ·

·    ·    ·    ·    ·    ·    ·    ·

·    ·    ·    ·    ·    ·    ·    ·

·    ·    ·    ·    ·    ·    ·    ·
```

If you were able to draw such a triangle, what kind of a triangle have you drawn?

19   *Geometric Constructions and Investigations with a Mira*

Name _____   Date _____

Worksheet 5

Symmetry Lines of Triangles *(continued)*

2. On the dot paper provided below, draw a picture, if possible, of a large triangle that has exactly two lines of symmetry. If you think the triangle you have drawn is correct, check it with a Mira.

If you were able to draw such a triangle, what kind of a triangle have you drawn?

Worksheet 5

Symmetry Lines of Triangles *(continued)*

3. On the dot paper provided below, draw a picture, if possible, of a large triangle that has exactly three lines of symmetry. If you think the triangle you have drawn is correct, check it with a Mira.

If you were able to draw such a triangle, what kind of a triangle have you drawn?

21   *Geometric Constructions and Investigations with a Mira*

Name _____   Date _____

Symmetry Lines of Triangles *(continued)*

4. On the dot paper provided below, draw a picture, if possible, of a large triangle that has zero lines of symmetry. If you think the triangle you have drawn is correct, check it with a Mira.

If you were able to draw such a triangle, what kind of a triangle have you drawn?

Lesson 6

Symmetry Lines of Quadrilaterals

Prerequisite Lessons

Lessons 1 and 4

Materials Needed

One copy of each of the following pages for each student: pages 25, 26, 27, and 28

One ruler or straightedge for each student

One Mira for each student

Directions for the Teacher

Distribute the worksheet pages and tell the students that as they draw quadrilaterals, they must have vertices at dots. Direct them to carefully make rather large quadrilaterals using a ruler or straightedge. Correct answers for the worksheet problems follow.

(1) a. Any isosceles trapezoid.

b. Any kite-shaped quadrilateral.

(2) a. Any rectangle, which is not a square.

b. Any rhombus, which is not a square.

(3) Not possible.

(4) Any square.

(5) Not possible.

(6) Many possible answers exist, including any non-isosceles trapezoid.

After the students have completed the worksheets, lead a discussion concerning the relationship between the number of symmetry lines and the type of quadrilateral. They should conclude that

(1) an isosceles trapezoid has exactly one line of symmetry,

(2) a kite-shaped figure (which is not a rhombus) has exactly one line of symmetry,

(3) both a rectangle and a rhombus (not a square) have exactly two lines of symmetry,

(4) there is no quadrilateral with exactly three lines of symmetry,

(5) a square has exactly four lines of symmetry,

(6) there is no quadrilateral that has more than four lines of symmetry, and

(7) non-isosceles trapezoids (and other quadrilaterals) have zero lines of symmetry.

A different format for these results follows.

Lines of Symmetry	Quadrilateral
0	a non-isosceles trapezoid, etc.
1	an isosceles trapezoid or a kite-shaped quadrilateral
2	a rectangle which is not a square, or a rhombus which is not a square
3	no quadrilateral
4	a square
>4	no quadrilateral

Name _____   Date _____

Worksheet 6

Symmetry Lines of Quadrilaterals

1. a. On the dot paper provided below, draw a picture, if possible, of a large trapezoid that has exactly one line of symmetry. Use a Mira to check to see that your drawing is correct.

b. On the dot paper provided below, draw a picture, if possible, of a large quadrilateral that
    (1) has exactly one line of symmetry and
    (2) is not a trapezoid.
Use the Mira to check to see that your drawing is correct.

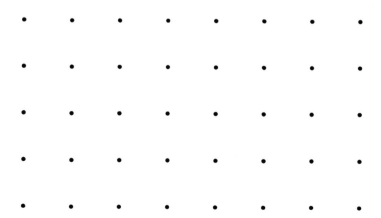

25   *Geometric Constructions and Investigations with a Mira*

Name _____   Date _____

Symmetry Lines of Quadrilaterals *(continued)*

2. a. On the dot paper provided below, draw a picture, if possible, of a large rectangle that has exactly two lines of symmetry. Use a Mira to check to see that your answer is correct.

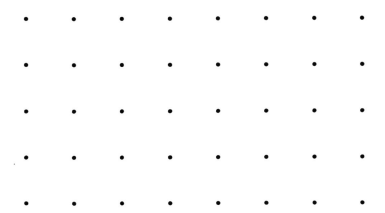

   b. On the dot paper provided below, draw a picture, if possible, of a large quadrilateral that
      (1) has exactly two lines of symmetry and
      (2) is not a rectangle.
   Use a Mira to check to see that your answer is correct.

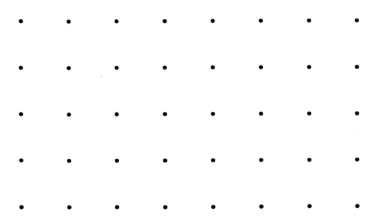

         Geometric Constructions and Investigations with a Mira

Worksheet 6

Symmetry Lines of Quadrilaterals *(continued)*

3. On the dot paper provided below, draw a picture, if possible, of a large quadrilateral that has exactly three lines of symmetry. Use a Mira to check to see that your answer is correct.

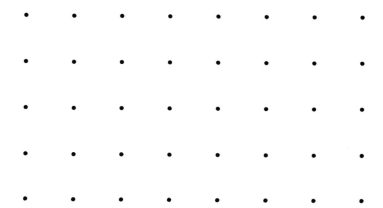

4. On the dot paper provided below, draw a picture, if possible, of a large quadrilateral that has exactly four lines of symmetry. Use a Mira to check to see that your answer is correct.

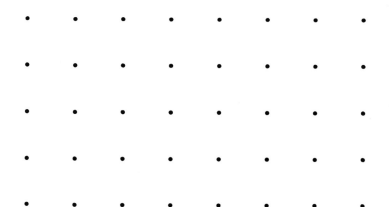

Name _____   Date _____

Worksheet 6

Symmetry Lines of Quadrilaterals *(continued)*

5. On the dot paper provided below, draw a picture, if possible, of a large quadrilateral that has exactly five lines of symmetry. Use a Mira to check to see that your answer is correct.

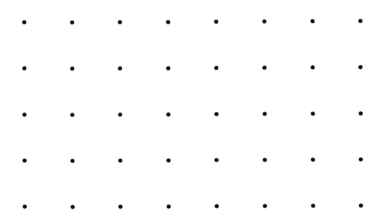

6. On the dot paper provided below, draw a picture, if possible, of a large quadrilateral that has exactly zero lines of symmetry. Use a Mira to check to see that your answer is correct.

Lesson 7
Mira Reflections of Letters I

Prerequisite Lessons

Lessons 1 and 4

Materials Needed

One copy of each of the following pages for each student: pages 30 and 31
One Mira for each student

Directions for the Teacher

Distribute the worksheet pages. Direct the students' attention to Problems 1 and 2. They should conclude that they can read the image of **EDDIE** but not the image of **MARY.** Have them proceed to Problems 3 and 4. Eventually, they should conclude that letters with a horizontal line of symmetry have readable images. You may need to give them a hint.

Name ——————————————————————— Date ———————————————————

Mira Reflections of Letters I

1. Place the Mira on the line and check the image of the word. Can you read the image easily?

———————————

E D D I E

2. Place the Mira on the line and check the image of the word. Can you read the image easily?

———————————

M A R Y

Worksheet 7

Mira Reflections of Letters I *(continued)*

3. Without using the Mira (don't cheat), try to predict which words will have a Mira image that is readable. Circle your answers. Now use your Mira to check.

_____

POD KID DOE DOG
BOX BY CODE TOW

4. Using the Mira, find which letters have readable images. Examine these letters carefully. Can you find a way to predict which ones will be readable?

_____

A B C D E F G H I J

Lesson 8

Mira Reflections of Letters II

Prerequisite Lessons

Lessons 1 and 4

Materials Needed

One copy of each of the following pages for each student: pages 33 and 34

One Mira for each student

Directions for the Teacher

Distribute the worksheet pages. Direct the students' attention to Problems 1 and 2. They should conclude that they can read the image of **TOM** but not of **FRED.** Have them proceed to Problem 3. They should conclude that letters with a vertical symmetry line have a readable image. You may need to give them a hint.

Name _____   Date _____

Worksheet 8

Mira Reflections of Letters II

1. Place the Mira on the line below and check the image of the word. Can you read it easily?

T

O

M

2. Place the Mira on the line below and check the image of the word. Can you read it easily?

F

R

E

D

33   *Geometric Constructions and Investigations with a Mira*

Name ——————————————————————— Date ———————————————————————

Worksheet 8

Mira Reflections of Letters II *(continued)*

3. Use the Mira to determine which letters have a readable image. Can you find a way to predict which ones will be readable?

A
B
C
D
E
F
G
H
I

 Geometric Constructions and Investigations with a Mira

Lesson 9

Constructing the
Perpendicular Bisector of a Segment

Prerequisite Lessons

Lessons 1 and 4

Materials Needed

One copy of each of the following pages for each student: pages 38, 39, and 40

One transparency of page 37

One Mira for each student

Directions for the Teacher

Place the transparency on the overhead projector and discuss what it means for a line to be the perpendicular bisector of a segment. In this specific situation, it should be concluded that $\overleftrightarrow{CD}$ is the perpendicular bisector of $\overline{AB}$ because

(1) E is the midpoint of $\overline{AB}$ and

(2) $\overleftrightarrow{CD} \perp \overline{AB}$.

Agree that in order for E to be the midpoint of $\overline{AB}$, it must be the case that $\overline{AE} \cong \overline{EB}$ and for $\overleftrightarrow{CD}$ to be perpendicular to $\overline{AB}$, it must be the case that $\angle AEC$ is congruent to $\angle BEC$.

Distribute the worksheet pages and direct the students' attention to Problem 1. Have them place the Mira in such a way that the image of point A is point B. Tell them to draw a line along the rebated edge of the Mira. Argue that this line is the perpendicular bisector of $\overline{AB}$, since the segment from A to the intersection of the Mira line and $\overline{AB}$ (segment on the near side of the Mira) is congruent to the segment from that point to B (segment on the far side of the Mira) and two adjacent angles are congruent. Have them construct the perpendicular bisectors of the other segments pictured in Problem 1. You might mention that the perpendicular bisector of a segment is actually a symmetry line of the segment.

Tell them to proceed to Problem 2. To construct the perpendicular bisector of the sides of a triangle, they must focus on each side separately and simply use the procedure established in Problem 1. After constructing the bisectors of the sides of the first two triangles, they might observe that in each case these bisectors intersect inside the triangle.

Have them proceed to the Problem 3. This time they should notice that the perpendicular bisectors of the sides of the triangle intersect outside the triangle. Lead a discussion about when the intersection of the perpendicular bisectors intersect inside the triangle (acute triangle) and when they intersect outside the triangle (obtuse triangle). Pose the question of the possibility of the three perpendicular bisectors meeting at a point on a side of a triangle (right triangle). Some students may wish to construct a right triangle and the perpendicular bisectors of the sides of the triangle to test the conjecture.

Transparency 9

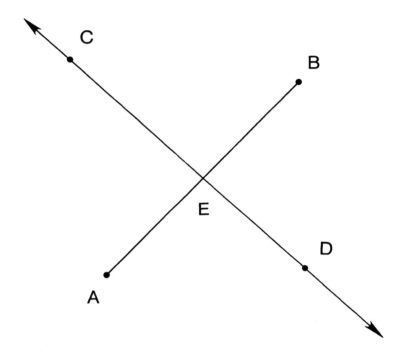

$\overleftrightarrow{CD}$ is the perpendicular bisector of $\overline{AB}$.

37   *Geometric Constructions and Investigations with a Mira*

Name _____   Date _____

Constructing the
Perpendicular Bisector of a Segment

1. Use a Mira to construct the perpendicular bisector of each segment pictured.

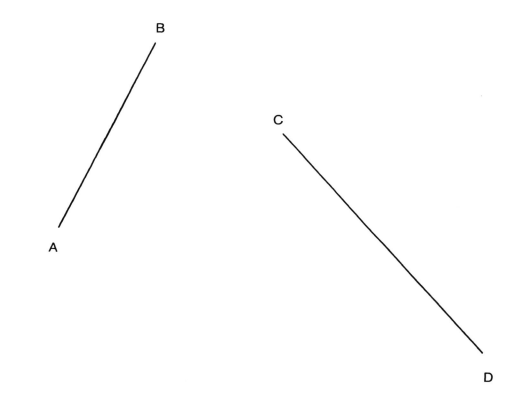

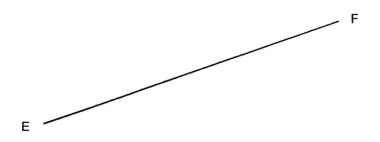

Worksheet 9

Constructing the Perpendicular
Bisector of a Segment *(continued)*

2. Construct the perpendicular bisectors of *all* the sides of the triangles pictured.

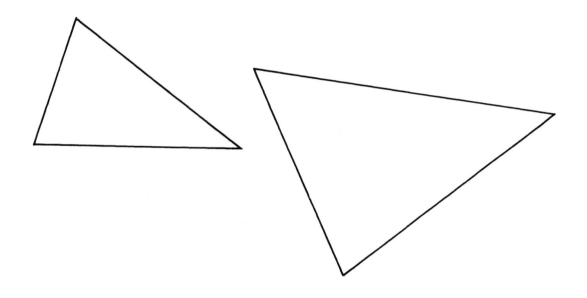

What do you notice about these perpendicular bisectors?

Constructing the Perpendicular
Bisector of a Segment *(continued)*

3. Construct the perpendicular bisectors of *all* the sides of the triangle pictured.

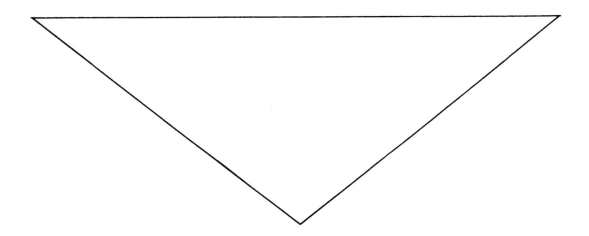

What do you notice about these perpendicular bisectors?

Lesson 10

Constructing a Line Through a Given Point and Perpendicular to a Given Line

Prerequisite Lessons

Lessons 1 and 9

Materials Needed

One copy of page 43 for each student

One transparency of page 42

One Mira for each student

Directions for the Teacher

Place the transparency on the overhead projector and indicate that in order for the lines to be perpendicular, a pair of adjacent angles must be congruent. Ask how the Mira could be used to ensure that two adjacent angles are congruent. The answer is by placing the Mira on line l and seeing that line m is its own reflection, or vice versa. Some teachers may wish to make student copies of the transparency master (but not transparencies) and have students use the Mira to check the perpendicularity of the lines.

Distribute the worksheet and direct the students' attention to Problem 1. Have them place the Mira across line l so that the portion of the line on the front side of the Mira matches in direction the portion of the line on the back side of the Mira. Argue that if students were to draw a line along the edge of the Mira, it would be perpendicular to l. Now have them slide the Mira along (keeping it perpendicular to l) until point A is on the rebated edge of the Mira and have them draw the line along the rebated edge of the Mira. Direct the students to Problem 2.

41

Transparency 10

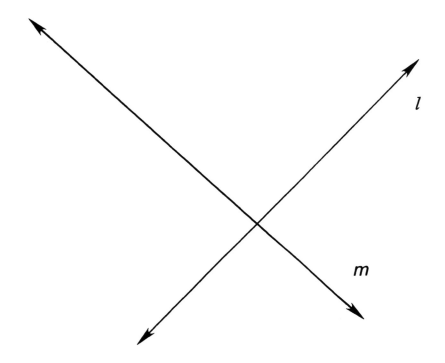

Line *l* is perpendicular to line *m*.

Geometric Constructions and Investigations with a Mira

Name _____   Date _____

Constructing a Line Through a Given Point and Perpendicular to a Given Line

1. With the Mira, construct a line through point A and perpendicular to line *l*.

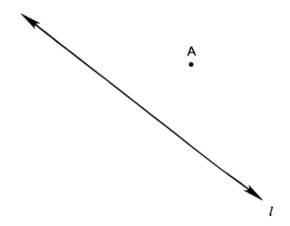

2. With the Mira, construct a line through point B and perpendicular to line *m*.

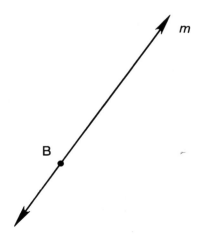

Lesson 11

Constructing Altitudes of Triangles, Parallelograms, and Trapezoids

Prerequisite Lessons

Lessons 1 and 10

Materials Needed

One copy of each of the following pages for each student: pages 46, 47, and 48

One Mira for each student

One ruler or straightedge for each student

Directions for the Teacher

A short review of Lesson 10 might be desirable. Students need to be able to construct a segment through a given point and perpendicular to a given segment. Suggest that the process for constructing a segment perpendicular to a given segment is identical to constructing a line perpendicular to a given line.

Distribute the first page of Worksheet 11 and discuss the definition of an altitude of a triangle. Have the students examine ΔABC. Tell them to first construct the altitude through B. Remind them that they must then construct a segment that passes through B and that is perpendicular to side $\overline{AC}$. A common mistake (difficulty) students have is trying to make point A the reflection image of point C. This will happen only if AB = BC, which is not true for this triangle. Have them construct the other two altitudes. Then have them proceed to ΔDEF. Note that the altitudes through E and F are exterior to the triangle, and that in each case sides $\overline{FD}$ and $\overline{DE}$ must be extended. Have the students use a ruler to extend these two sides. Here is the completed version of this problem as it will appear:

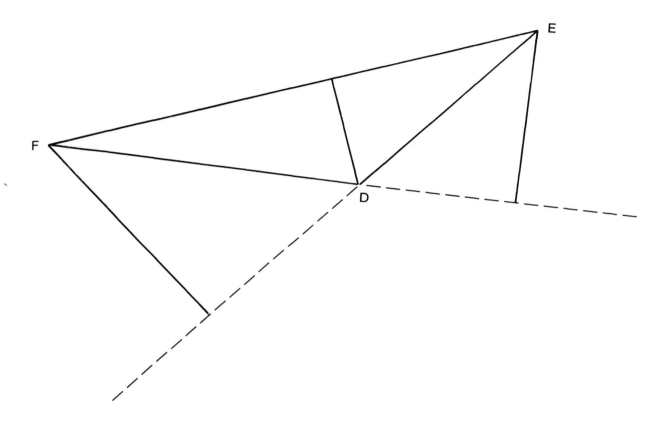

Have students proceed to ΔGHI. This is a right triangle, so $\overline{HG}$ and $\overline{HI}$ are themselves both sides and altitudes of the triangle. They need only draw the altitude through H.

Distribute the second page of Worksheet 11 and discuss the definition of an altitude of a parallelogram. Emphasize that a base must be determined before an altitude can be considered. To emphasize the fact that the bottom side need not always be the base, classify $\overline{AB}$ as the base for parallelogram ABCD and have students use the Mira to draw an altitude. They may choose to draw this altitude through point D, but that is not required. Let them choose the bases for the other two parallelograms and have them draw the required altitudes. Provide individual help as needed.

Distribute the third page of Worksheet 11. Have the students draw altitudes as directed. Provide individual help as needed.

Worksheet 11

Constructing Altitudes of Triangles, Parallelograms, and Trapezoids

1. An *altitude* of a triangle is a segment that has as one end point a vertex of a triangle, that has as the other end point a point on the side opposite this vertex (sometimes the side must be extended), and that is perpendicular to that side. Use a Mira to find all three altitudes of the triangles pictured below.

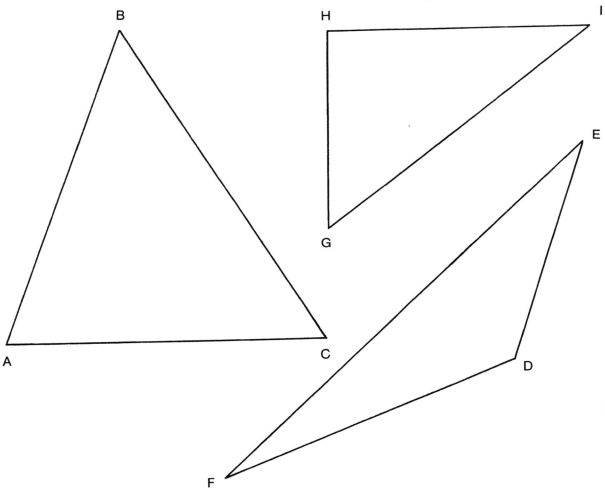

Worksheet 11

Constructing Altitudes of Triangles, Parallelograms, and Trapezoids *(continued)*

2. In the case of a parallelogram, it is common to classify one side of the parallelogram as the base. Then an altitude of a parallelogram is a segment that has one end point on the base, the other end point on the side opposite the base (possibly extended), and is perpendicular to the base. For each parallelogram pictured below, classify one side as the base and use a Mira to draw an altitude to that base.

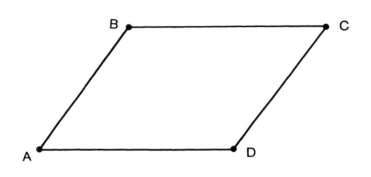

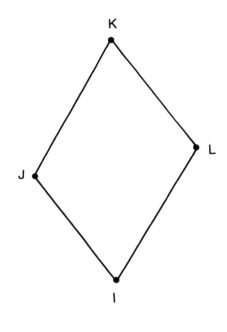

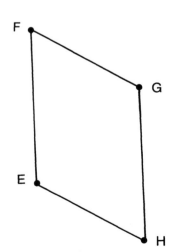

Worksheet 11

Constructing Altitudes of Triangles, Parallelograms, and Trapezoids *(continued)*

3. The two parallel sides of a trapezoid are called the bases. An altitude of a trapezoid is a segment that has an end point on each of the two bases (possibly extended) and is perpendicular to the bases. For each trapezoid pictured below, use a Mira to draw an altitude.

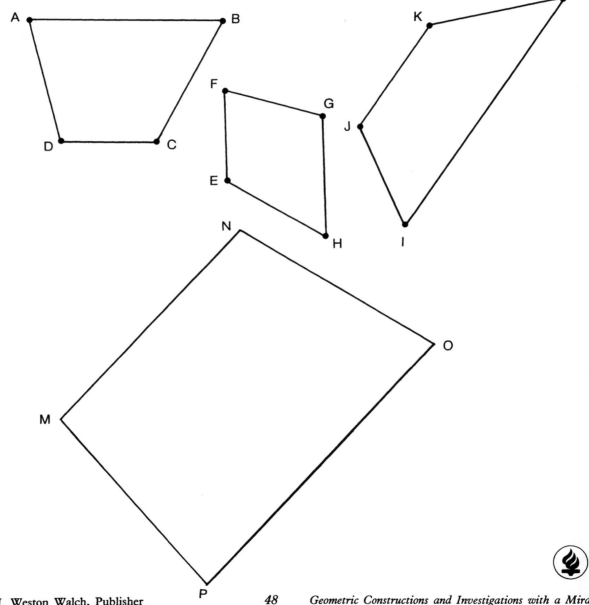

Lesson 12

Bisecting Angles

Prerequisite Lessons

Lesson 1

Materials Needed

One copy of each of the following pages for each student: pages 50, 51, and 52

One Mira for each student

Directions for the Teacher

Distribute the worksheet pages and direct the students' attention to Problem 1a. Have them place the Mira so that

(1) point B is along the edge of the Mira, and

(2) the image of $\overrightarrow{BA}$ matches $\overrightarrow{BC}$ in direction, or the image of $\overrightarrow{BC}$ matches $\overrightarrow{BA}$ in direction.

Then have students draw a ray from B toward the interior of the angle. Have them proceed similarly with $\angle DEF$.

Direct students' attention to Problem 2 and Problem 3. They should bisect the angles of each triangle and discover that the three angle bisectors intersect at a point within the triangle. Unless they are very careful, they may think the three angle bisectors form a very small triangle within the given triangle.

Worksheet 12

Bisecting Angles

1. Use a Mira to bisect the angles.

   a.

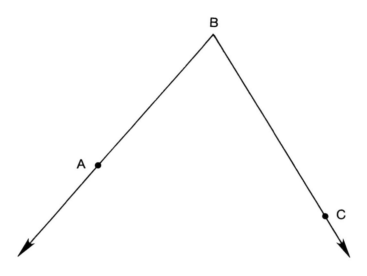

   b.

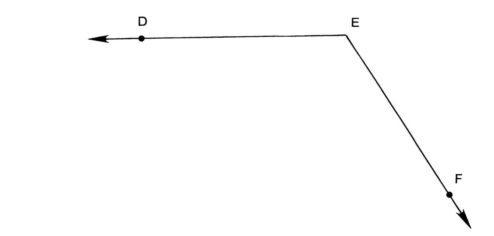

                   Geometric Constructions and Investigations with a Mira

Worksheet 12

Bisecting Angles *(continued)*

2. Use a Mira to bisect all of the angles of the triangles pictured below.

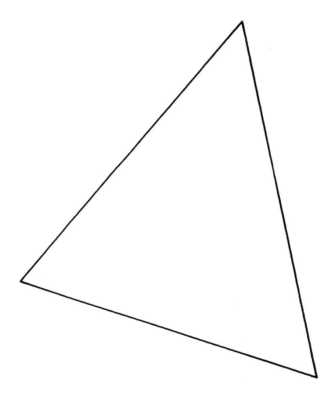

What do you notice about the angle bisectors within each triangle?

51   *Geometric Constructions and Investigations with a Mira*

Worksheet 12

Bisecting Angles *(continued)*

3. Use a Mira to bisect all of the angles of the triangles pictured below.

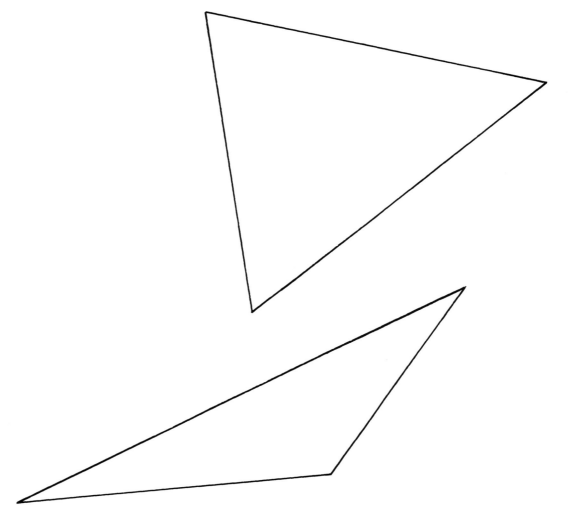

What do you notice about the angle bisectors within each triangle?

Lesson 13

Circles and Arcs

Prerequisite Lessons

Lessons 1 and 4

Materials Needed

One copy of page 54 for each student

One Mira for each student

Directions for the Teacher

Distribute the worksheet and have the students start working on the problems presented there. They probably will be able to complete Problems 1, 2, and 3 without assistance. When they have finished Problem 1, you might want to point out that the line through the centers of the circles is actually the symmetry line. As they get to Problem 4, you will probably need to tell them that to quadrasect the arc, they will need to separate the arc into four congruent arcs. This can be done by bisecting the arc and then bisecting the two smaller arcs.

Name _____   Date _____

Worksheet 13

Circles and Arcs

1. Use the Mira to construct the line that passes through the centers of both circles.

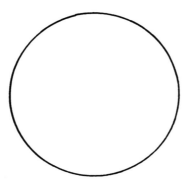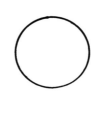

2. Use the Mira to find the center of the circle.

4. Use the Mira to quadrasect the arc.

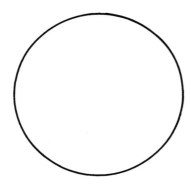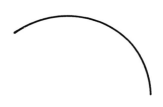

3. Use the Mira to bisect the arc.

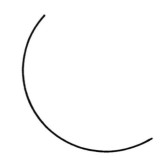

54   *Geometric Constructions and Investigations with a Mira*

Lesson 14

Congruence

Prerequisite Lessons

Lesson 1

Materials Needed

One copy of each of the following pages for each student: pages 56 and 57

One blank transparency and one marking pen for each student

One Mira for each student

Directions for the Teacher

Distribute both worksheet pages. Have the students complete Problems 1 and 2. For Problem 3, have them trace $\overline{AB}$ on a blank transparency and then match this copy of $\overline{AB}$ to each of the other segments pictured. They should decide that these segments are all congruent to $\overline{AB}$. Then have students find out which segments can be reflected onto $\overline{AB}$ ($\overline{CD}$, $\overline{GH}$, and $\overline{IJ}$). After this problem has been completed, lead a discussion in which the following generalizations are made:

(1) The Mira can be used to find out whether any two circles (in the same plane) are congruent.

(2) It may or may not be possible to use a single reflection with a Mira to find out whether two segments are congruent.

Name _____   Date _____

Worksheet 14

Congruence

1. Use the Mira to answer the following questions.

    a. Which circles are congruent to circle 1? _____

    b. Which circles are congruent to circle 2? _____

    c. Which circles are congruent to circle 3? _____

    d. Which circles are congruent to circle 4? _____

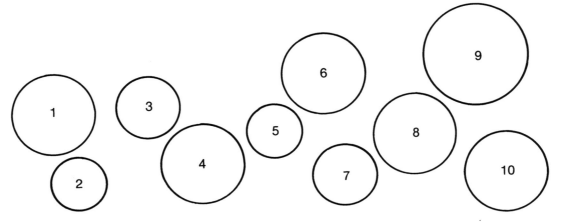

2. Use the Mira to decide which of the segments pictured are congruent to $\overline{AB}$.

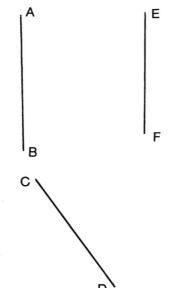

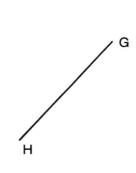

Worksheet 14

Congruence *(continued)*

3. All of the segments pictured below are congruent to $\overline{AB}$. Use a blank transparency and a marking pen to confirm this fact. Then, use the Mira to find out which ones can be reflected onto $\overline{AB}$ using a single reflection.

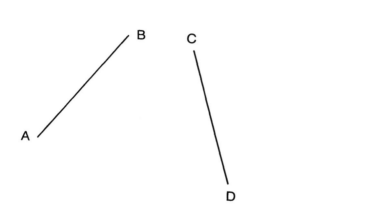

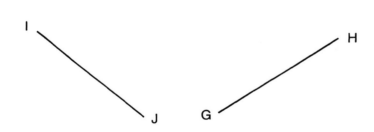

Lesson 15

Constructing an Equilateral Triangle

Prerequisite Lessons

Lessons 1, 4, and 9

Materials Needed

One copy of each of the following pages for each student: pages 60 and 61

One ruler or straightedge for each student

One Mira for each student

Directions for the Teacher

Distribute the worksheet pages and direct your students to Problem 1. From working that problem, they should conclude that any point on the perpendicular bisector of a segment is equally distant from the end points of the segment (the segments are congruent).

Next, have students proceed to Problem 2. They may need several hints for this construction. Here are the construction steps:

(1) Construct the perpendicular bisector of $\overline{AB}$.

(2) Place the Mira so that A is along the rebated edge of the Mira.

(3) Rotate the Mira (keeping A along the rebated edge) until the image of B falls on the perpendicular bisector.

(4) Reach behind the Mira and put a dot on the image point of B and call the new point C.

(5) Draw $\overline{AC}$ and $\overline{BC}$.

This construction is appropriate because students found C so that $\overline{AB} \cong \overline{AC}$. Then, since C is on the perpendicular bisector of $\overline{AB}$, $\overline{AC} \cong \overline{BC}$.

Concerning the construction of the equilateral triangle, give as many hints as necessary. This is a very difficult construction.

Worksheet 15

Constructing an Equilateral Triangle

1. (a) Using a Mira, construct the perpendicular bisector of $\overline{AB}$.

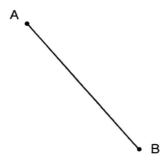

(b) Next, select a point on the perpendicular bisector, label it C, and draw $\overline{AC}$ and $\overline{BC}$. Use the Mira to compare the lengths of $\overline{AC}$ and $\overline{BC}$. What do you find?

(c) Next, select another point on the perpendicular bisector, label it D, and draw $\overline{AD}$ and $\overline{BD}$. Use the Mira to compare the lengths of $\overline{AD}$ and $\overline{BD}$. What do you find?

(d) What is your conclusion about the distances from a point on the perpendicular bisector of a segment to the two end points of the segment?

Worksheet 15

Constructing an Equilateral Triangle *(continued)*

2. Use the Mira to construct an equilateral triangle with $\overline{AB}$ as one side of this triangle.

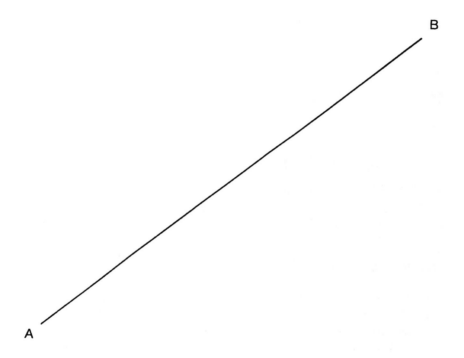

61 *Geometric Constructions and Investigations with a Mira*

Lesson 16

Constructing Angles
with a Given Measure

Prerequisite Lessons

Lessons 1, 9, and 15

Materials Needed

One copy of each of the following pages for each student: pages 63, 64, and 65

One Mira for each student

Directions for the Teacher

Distribute the worksheet pages. Problems 1, 2, and 3 are fairly easy. For Problems 1 and 2, you may need to give the hint that each angle of an equilateral triangle has measure 60°. Bisecting one of the 60° angles will produce a 30° angle. Since right angles are formed by perpendicular lines and since $\frac{1}{2} \cdot 90 = 45$, it is easy to construct an angle of measure 45°. For Problem 4, you might want to hint that $75 = 45 + 30$ or $75 = 90 - 15$. A 30-60-90 triangle can be constructed in the process of bisecting an angle of an equilateral triangle. Constructing a 45-45-90 triangle is fairly easy since a triangle of this type is both a right triangle and an isosceles triangle.

Name ———————————————————— Date ————————————————————

Constructing Angles
with a Given Measure

1. Use the Mira to construct an angle with measure 60°.

2. Use the Mira to construct an angle with measure 30°.

         Geometric Constructions and Investigations with a Mira

Worksheet 16

Constructing Angles with
a Given Measure *(continued)*

3. Use the Mira to construct an angle with measure 45°.

4. Use the Mira to construct an angle with measure 75°.

Constructing Angles with
a Given Measure *(continued)*

5. Use the Mira to construct a 30-60-90 triangle (a triangle where the measures of the angles are 30°, 60°, and 90°).

6. Use the Mira to construct a 45-45-90 triangle.

Lesson 17

Reflecting Triangles II

Prerequisite Lessons

Lessons 1, 2, and 12

Materials Needed

One copy of each of the following pages for each student: pages 71 and 72

One Mira for each student

One ruler or straightedge for each student

Directions for the Teacher

Distribute the first page of Worksheet 17 and have your students start with the directions given there. Provide individual help as needed. There are two possible reflections for this problem as shown in the next two figures.

First Solution

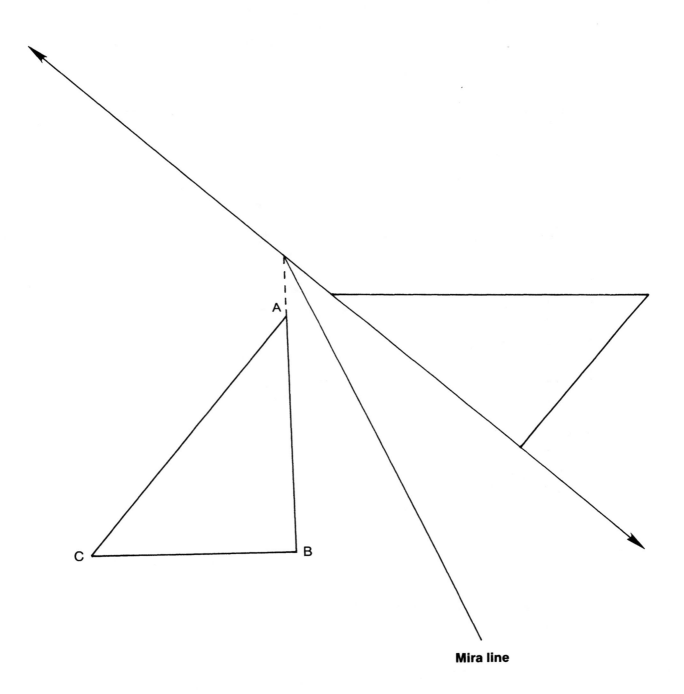

Mira line

Second Solution

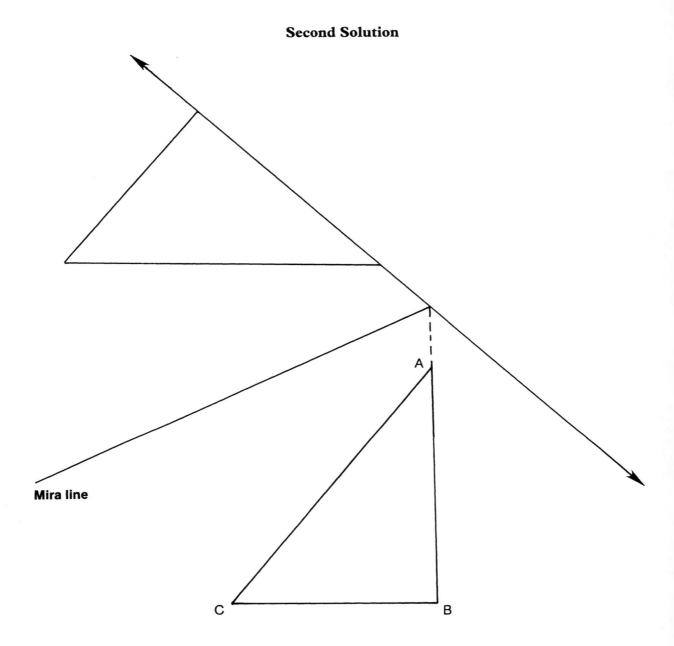

Mira line

The students should discover that the Mira reflection line is the bisector of an angle formed by the original line and the extension of $\overline{AB}$. You may need to give several hints about this generalization.

Next, distribute the second page of worksheet 17 and have students follow the directions given there. They may have a little difficulty finding *two* ways to reflect the triangle so that $\overline{AB}$ falls on the line. Provide assistance as needed.

Now have the students proceed as they did for the first worksheet. Specifically have them

(1) extend $\overline{AB}$ so that the extension intersects the line at a point,

(2) put the Mira in so that △ABC matches one of the new triangles; draw along the Mira, and

(3) put the Mira in so that △ABC matches the other new triangle; and draw along the Mira.

Here is how student worksheets should appear:

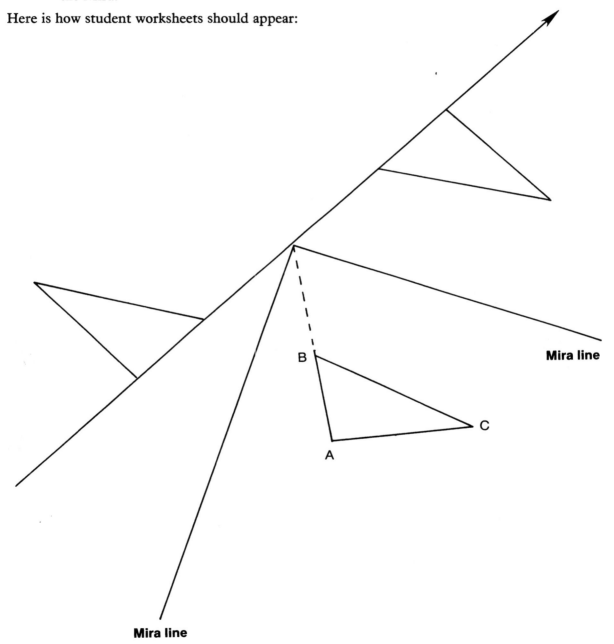

Students should conclude that in both cases the Mira line bisects an angle formed by the given line and the extension of $\overline{AB}$. Next ask them about the lines formed by the two Mira lines (it is a right angle). They can check this by matching this angle with an angle of an index card or an ordinary $8\frac{1}{2}''$ by $11''$ piece of paper.

Worksheet 17

Reflecting Triangles II

Place the Mira between the triangle and the line and move it around until the image of $\overline{AB}$ falls on the line. Reach behind the Mira and mark the points that correspond to A, B, and C; draw the triangle. Next use a straightedge to extend $\overline{AB}$ until the extension intersects the line. Then place the Mira in the position where $\triangle ABC$ matches the new triangle and draw the Mira line. What do you notice about the Mira line?

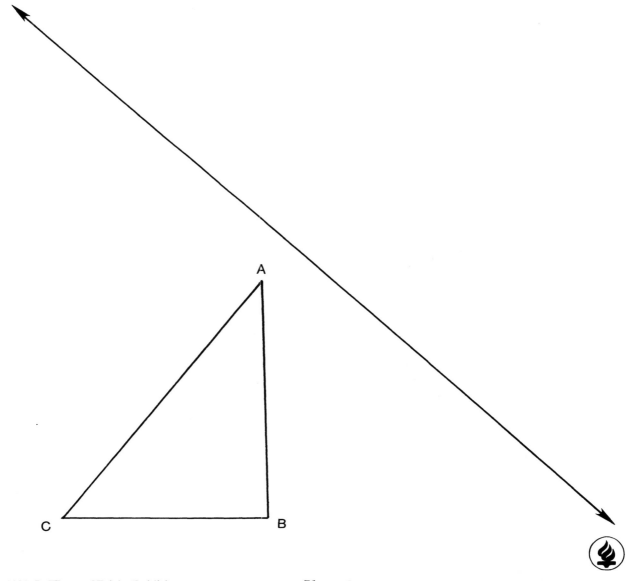

Name _____   Date _____

Worksheet 17

Reflecting Triangles II *(continued)*

Place the Mira between the triangle and the line and move it around until the image of $\overline{AB}$ falls on the line. Reach behind the Mira and mark the points that correspond to A, B, and C. Draw the new triangle. Repeat the process so that the image of $\overline{AB}$ falls on the line in a different place.

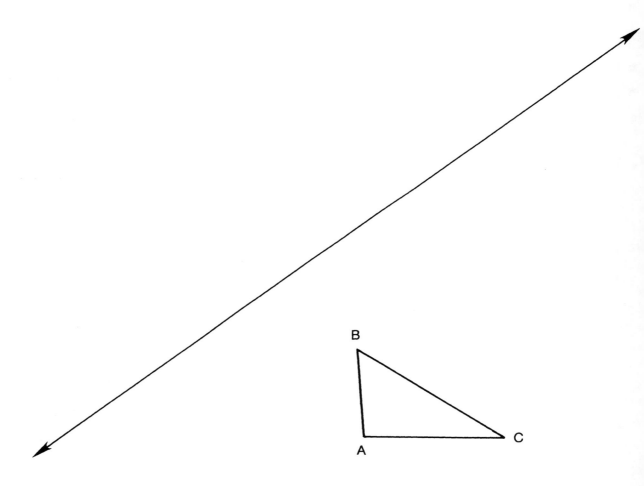

72   *Geometric Constructions and Investigations with a Mi*

Lesson 18

Constructing a Line Through a Given Point and Parallel to a Given Line

Prerequisite Lessons

Lesson 1 and 10

Materials Needed

One copy of each of the following pages for each student: pages 74, 75, and 76

One Mira for each student

Directions for the Teacher

Distribute the first page of Worksheet 18. Problems 1 and 2 illustrate a classic error that students make when asked to use the Mira to determine if two lines are parallel. Any two coplanar lines, parallel or not, are reflections of each other.

Distribute the second and third pages of Worksheet 18. Problem 3 illlustrates the correct strategy to use. With Problem 4, the students should place the Mira perpendicular to line a. They should see that lines a, c, and e are their own reflections with this Mira position.

In problem 5, a line perpendicular to line k through point A is drawn, then another line perpendicular to this line is drawn through point A. Do likewise for point B.

In problem 6, draw an arbitrary auxiliary line, then draw the lines through A,B, C, and D perpendicular to the auxiliary line.

Name _____   Date _____

Constructing a Line Through a Given Point and Parallel to a Given Line

1. Use the Mira to reflect line m onto line k.

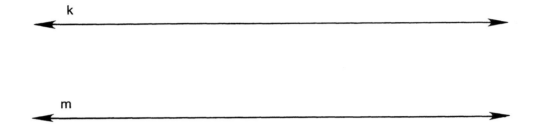

Do lines m and k appear to be parallel?

2. Use the Mira to reflect line t onto line s.

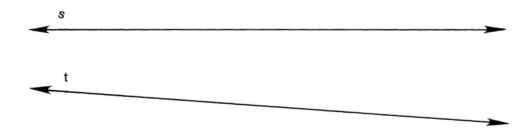

Do lines t and s appear to be parallel?

Conclusion: Any two coplanar lines, parallel or not, are reflections of each other with a Mira.

Name _____   Date _____

Worksheet 18

Constructing a Line Through a Given Point and Parallel to a Given Line *(continued)*

3. Place your Mira perpendicular to line m in Problem 1. Observe that both lines m and k are reflected on themselves.

Place your Mira perpendicular to line t in Problem 2. Observe that line t reflects on itself, but that line s does not reflect on itself.

Important Generalization

If two lines in the same plane are perpendicular to the same line, they are parallel.

4. Use the Mira and the above generalization to see which lines are parallel to line a.

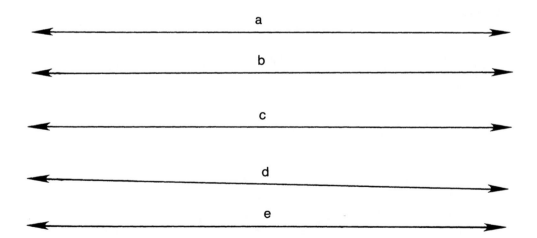

Constructing a Line Through a Given Point and Parallel to a Given Line *(continued)*

5. Use the Mira to construct line l through point A that is parallel to line k. Use the Mira to construct line m through point B that is parallel to line k. What statement can be made about lines l and m?

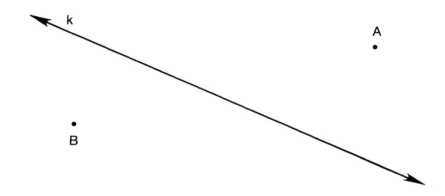

6. Use the Mira to construct a line through A, a line through B, a line through C, and a line through D, so that the four lines are parallel to each other.

         Geometric Constructions and Investigations with a Mira

Lesson 19

Constructing Quadrilaterals I

Prerequisite Lessons

Lessons 1, 10, and 18

Materials Needed

One copy of each of the following pages for each student: pages 80, 81, and 82

One transparency of page 79

One Mira for each student

Directions for the Teacher

Place the transparency on the overhead projector and go through the material given there. Leave the transparency on the overhead projector so the students may refer to it. Distribute the three pages of Worksheet 19. Here are ways that these constructions can be made:

Problem 1 (This is a review of the strategy developed in Lesson 18.)

(1) Construct a line through A that is perpendicular to *l*.

(2) Construct a line through A that is perpendicular to the line drawn in (1).

Problem 2

(1) Select an arbitrary point C that is not on $\overline{AB}$ and, using the procedure illustrated in Problem 1, construct a line that is parallel to $\overline{AB}$ and that passes through C.

(2) Draw $\overline{BC}$.

(3) Select another point D on the constructed line so that $\overline{CD}$ is not congruent to $\overline{AB}$ and so that D is on the same side of $\overleftrightarrow{BC}$ as A.

(4) Draw $\overline{AD}$. The quadrilateral ABCD is a trapezoid.

Problem 3

(1) Draw a line *l*, parallel to $\overline{AB}$.

(2) Select a point C on *l* so that ∠ABC is not a right angle. Draw $\overline{BC}$.

(3) Draw a line through A that is parallel to $\overline{BC}$.

(4) Call the intersection of these constructed nonparallel lines D. Quadrilateral ABCD is then a parallelogram.

Problem 4

(1) Extend $\overline{AB}$ in both directions.

(2) Construct a line that is perpendicular to $\overline{AB}$ and that passes through B. Select a point C on the constructed line where $\overline{AB} \neq \overline{BC}$.

(3) Construct a line through C parallel to $\overline{AB}$. Also, construct a line through A that is perpendicular to $\overline{AB}$. Call the intersection of these two constructed lines D.

(4) Quadrilateral ABCD is a rectangle that is not a square.

Problem 5

(1) Extend $\overline{AB}$ in both directions.

(2) Construct a line that is perpendicular to $\overline{AB}$ and that passes through B.

(3) Use the Mira to find a point C on this line so that $\overline{AB} \cong \overline{BC}$.

(4) Construct a line that passes through C and that is parallel to $\overline{AB}$.

(5) Construct a line that passes through A and that is perpendicular to $\overline{AB}$.

(6) Name the intersection of the last two lines D. Quadrilateral ABCD is then a square.

As the students work these problems, provide assistance as needed. The constructions *can* be done in ways other than those described above.

Transparency 19

Definitions

A *trapezoid* is a quadrilateral with exactly one pair of parallel sides.

A *parallelogram* is a quadrilateral with two pairs of parallel sides.

A *rectangle* is a parallelogram (two pairs of parallel sides) with at least one right angle.

A *square* is a rectangle with at least one pair of adjacent congruent sides.

Important Generalization

If two lines are in the same plane and are perpendicular to the same line, they are parallel.

Worksheet 19

Constructing Quadrilaterals I

1. Use the Mira to construct a line that is parallel to line *l* and that passes through A.

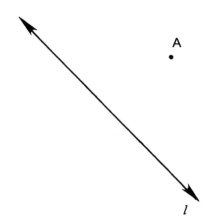

2. Use the Mira to construct a trapezoid that has $\overline{AB}$ as one of the parallel sides.

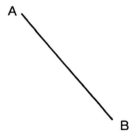

 Geometric Constructions and Investigations with a Mira

Worksheet 19

Constructing Quadrilaterals I *(continued)*

3. Use the Mira to construct a parallelogram that is not a rectangle and that has $\overline{AB}$ as one side.

4. Use the Mira to construct a rectangle that is not a square and that has $\overline{AB}$ as one side.

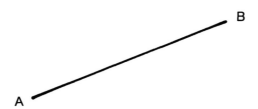

                   Geometric Constructions and Investigations with a Mira

Worksheet 19

Constructing Quadrilaterals I *(continued)*

5. Use the Mira to construct a square that has $\overline{AB}$ as one side.

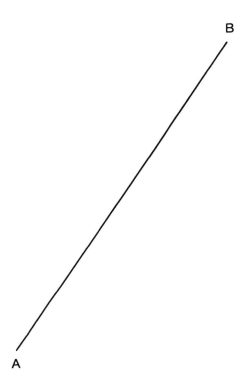

               Geometric Constructions and Investigations with a Mira

Lesson 20

Properties of
Diagonals of Quadrilaterals

Prerequisite Lessons

Lessons 1, 4, and 9

Materials Needed

One copy of each of the following pages for each student: pages 86, 87, and 88

One transparency of page 85

One Mira for each student

Directions for the Teacher

Distribute the pages of Worksheet 20. For the first problem, direct the students to place the Mira so that E is along the edge of the Mira. Tell them to turn the Mira in an effort to make point A match point C. They will be able to do this so E is the midpoint of $\overline{AC}$. In a similar way, they should find that E is the midpoint of $\overline{BD}$. This confirms that, in this case, the diagonals bisect each other. Next, have students place the Mira at E and turn the Mira so that the edge of the Mira is perpendicular to $\overline{AC}$. They will find that the Mira line does not correspond to $\overline{BD}$, so $\overline{BD}$ is not perpendicular to $\overline{AC}$. They should arrive at comparable conclusions for quadrilateral FGHI.

Have students proceed in a similar way with Problem 2. For these rectangles, they should conclude that the diagonals are congruent and bisect each other but are not perpendicular. For Problem 3, they should immediately conclude that the diagonals are perpendicular and bisect each other. To conclude that the diagonals are also congruent, students may use the Mira to first conclude that $\overline{BE} \cong \overline{CE}$. Then, since E is the midpoint of both $\overline{AC}$ and $\overline{BD}$, they should conclude that $\overline{AC} \cong \overline{BD}$. In a comparable way, they may conclude that the diagonals of quadrilateral FGHI bisect each other. After the students have finished the worksheets, put the transparency on the overhead projector and go through the generalizations there.

Transparency 20

The diagonals of a parallelogram bisect each other but are not necessarily congruent and are not necessarily perpendicular.

The diagonals of a rectangle bisect each other and are congruent but are not necessarily perpendicular.

The diagonals of a square bisect each other, are congruent, and are perpendicular.

 Geometric Constructions and Investigations with a Mira

Name _____   Date _____

Properties of
Diagonals of Quadrilaterals

1. Use the Mira to help you answer the questions below.

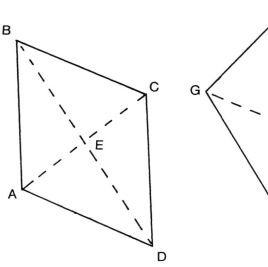
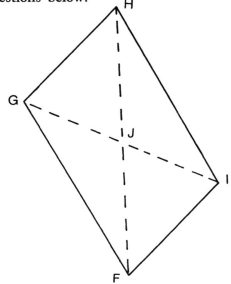

   a. Do the diagonals of the parallelograms bisect each other?   _____

   b. Are the diagonals of the parallelograms perpendicular?   _____

   c. Are the diagonals of the parallelograms congruent?   _____

       Geometric Constructions and Investigations with a Mira

Worksheet 20

Properties of Diagonals
of Quadrilaterals *(continued)*

2. Use the Mira to help you answer the questions below.

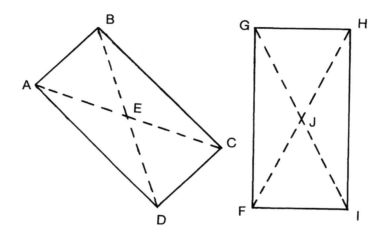

    a. Do the diagonals of the rectangles bisect each other? _____

    b. Are the diagonals of the rectangles perpendicular? _____

    c. Are the diagonals of the rectangles congruent? _____

Properties of Diagonals
of Quadrilaterals *(continued)*

3. Use the Mira to answer the questions below.

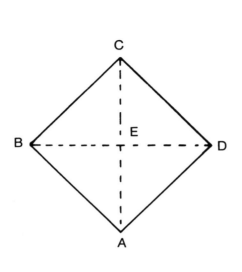

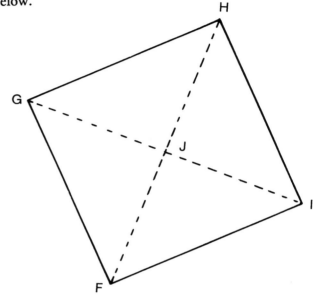

    a. Do the diagonals of the squares bisect each other?   _____

    b. Are the diagonals of the squares perpendicular?   _____

    c. Are the diagonals of the squares congruent?   _____

Lesson 21

Constructing Quadrilaterals II

Prerequisite Lessons

Lessons 1, 4, 9, and 20

Materials Needed

One copy of each of the following pages for each student: pages 91 and 92

One transparency of page 85 (Lesson 20)

One Mira for each student

Directions for the Teacher

Place the transparency on the overhead projector. Review the generalizations made there. Leave the transparency on so that students can refer to it. Distribute the pages of Worksheet 21. Here is how the constructions can be made:

Problem 1

(1) Draw an arbitrary segment, $\overline{AC}$.

(2) Find the midpoint of $\overline{AC}$ by using the Mira to make the image of A match point C. Call this midpoint E.

(3) Place the edge of the Mira on E, so that the edge of the Mira does not coincide with $\overline{AC}$ and is not perpendicular to $\overline{AC}$. Draw the Mira line.

(4) Select some point B on this line so that $\overline{BE}$ is not congruent to $\overline{AE}$.

(5) Find a point D, such that E is between B and D and $\overline{BE} \cong \overline{ED}$.

(6) Then quadrilateral ABCD (or ADCB) is a parallelogram, which is not a rectangle.

Problem 2

(1) Draw an arbitrary segment, $\overline{AC}$.

(2) Find the midpoint of $\overline{AC}$ by using the Mira to make the image of A match point C. Call this midpoint E.

(3) Place the edge of the Mira on E, so that the edge of the Mira does not coincide with $\overline{AC}$ and is not perpendicular to $\overline{AC}$. Draw the Mira line.

(4) Select some point B on this line so that $\overline{BE} \cong \overline{AE}$.

(5) Find a point D such that E is between B and D and $\overline{BE} \cong \overline{ED}$.

(6) Then quadrilateral ABCD (or ADCB) is a rectangle, which is not a square.

Problem 3

(1) Draw an arbitrary segment, $\overline{AC}$.

(2) Construct the line that is the perpendicular bisector of $\overline{AC}$. Let E be the midpoint of $\overline{AC}$.

(3) Find a point B on this line so that $\overline{AE} \cong \overline{BE}$.

(4) Find a point D such that E is between B and D and $\overline{BE} \cong \overline{ED}$.

(5) Then quadrilateral ABCD (or ADCB) is a square.

Provide individual assistance as needed. It should be pointed out that for Problem 1 the diagonals are constructed so that these diagonals bisect each other; for Problem 2 the diagonals are constructed so that these diagonals bisect each other and are congruent; and for Problem 3, the diagonals are constructed so that the diagonals bisect each other, are congruent, and are perpendicular.

Worksheet 21

Constructing Quadrilaterals II

1. Use a Mira to construct a parallelogram that is not a rectangle. Do this by first constructing the diagonals of the parallelogram.

2. Use a Mira to construct a rectangle that is not a square. Do this by first constructing the diagonals of the rectangle.

Worksheet 21

Constructing Quadrilaterals II *(continued)*

3. Use a Mira to construct a square. Do this by first constructing the diagonals.

 Geometric Constructions and Investigations with a Mira

Notes